Biff had to get the bats.

They are in the shed.

1

Biff had to go to the shed.

Chip had to go with her.

The shed had bats and mats.

It had rings and lots of things.

They had a shock.

Shh! It is a robin.

The robin was in a bush.

The robin had eggs in the bush.

The robin sat on the eggs.

Quick! Tell Mrs May.

Biff and Chip ran back to tell Mrs May.

Mrs May put up a big net.

The robin sat on her eggs.

She had chicks.

She fed her chicks.

The chicks got big.